S0-BBU-039

Moses in Egypt

Moses in Egypt

Written by
Gary Burge

Illustrated by
Karen Pritchett

Publications International, Ltd.

Long ago, there was a terrible famine in the land of Israel. The crops would not grow and the people were starving. So they decided to move to Egypt. There, the Israelites lived in peace for more than 400 years.

Now in Egypt, kings were called Pharaohs. The Pharaoh hated the Israelites. He made them slaves and forced them to build palaces for him.

Then he ordered that all their newborn children should die.

One day a beautiful baby boy was born into an Israelite family. His mother and father hid the baby. They were afraid the Pharaoh's soldiers would find him and take him away. But the baby's mother had an idea.

"I am going to put him in a small straw boat in the river," she said. "The soldiers will never look there." The baby's sister Miriam stayed to keep watch over her little brother.

That very day, Pharaoh's daughter came to the river for a bath, and she saw the little straw boat!

"What is that basket in the water?" she asked. When she looked into the straw basket she saw a crying baby. The princess picked him up and held him. "I will call him Moses," she said.

Then the princess had an idea. "Let's find a nurse to take care of him," she said. Miriam heard this and rushed home. Soon she returned to the river with her mother.

"Take this child and raise him for me," the princess told Moses' mother. "You must return him to me when he is grown."

When Moses was grown, he went to Pharaoh's palace to become the son of Pharaoh's daughter. There he learned to be an Egyptian soldier.

One day, Moses saw an Egyptian soldier beating an Israelite slave. This made Moses very angry, so he told the soldier to stop. When the soldier refused, Moses fought and killed him.

Pharaoh was furious that Moses had killed a soldier to defend Israelite slaves. Soldiers were hunting for Moses everywhere.

Moses ran away from Egypt to the land of Midian. There, he became a shepherd. One afternoon, while near a mountain called Mt. Sinai, he saw a bush that burned, but it never burned up. Then a voice came from the bush.

"Moses, take off your sandals! This is holy ground!" it said. "I am God, the God of your people."

Moses was so afraid! The Lord continued to speak, "I am sending you to save my people from Pharaoh. I have chosen a special land for them. You will lead them there."

Moses returned to Egypt and found his brother Aaron. Together with Aaron, Moses told the Israelites, "God will set you free."

The people were filled with joy. But the Pharaoh laughed when Aaron and Moses came to him. "I don't care about your God," Pharaoh said.

So Moses and Aaron used God's power to perform great wonders. They turned Aaron's staff into a snake; they turned river water into blood; they even filled Egypt with frogs, gnats, flies, and grasshoppers.

Then Moses and Aaron called for a thunderstorm and darkness. But still Pharaoh refused to let the Israelites go.

Then God told Moses to warn Pharaoh one last time. "Let my people go or the firstborn of every family will die this night." But Pharaoh's heart was as hard as stone.

Moses told the Israelites to pack. "Tonight we leave," he said. "Make a special meal of lamb and bread and bitter spices to remind you of what God is doing for us. Mark your doors with the blood of a lamb."

Late that night, an angel came to Egypt. The angel did not stop at the houses marked with lamb's blood. But every other firstborn died. Even Pharaoh's son died. But the firstborn of Israel were safe.

Soon the Egyptians were begging the Israelites, "Leave us before things get worse!" And in the morning, the Israelites were set free.

Large caravans of people followed Moses and Aaron out of Egypt. God set a huge cloud in front of the Israelites for them to follow.

Back in Egypt, Pharaoh changed his mind. "Why did we let the slaves escape?" he yelled at his soldiers. Pharaoh jumped into his chariot. "Chase them! I will punish them."

The Israelites were almost out of Egypt when they came to a huge lake. Scouts came to Moses saying, "Pharaoh and his army are coming! We're trapped!"

The people cried out in fear. But Moses told them to be quiet. "Do not be afraid. God will fight for you."

Moses turned toward the sea and raised his staff in the air, as God told him to do. Suddenly the sea opened. The Israelites ran along the seabed to the other shore.

Then they turned to look back. Egyptian chariots were chasing them! Moses waited for the chariots to enter the path. Then God told him to raise his staff. The walls of water crashed down onto the Egyptians.

"God has saved us," they said as they raised their hands to God. "God has set us free."

The End